Vocabulary Flashcards

California

Focus on Life Science

PEARSON

Prentice Hall

Boston, Massachusetts
Upper Saddle River, New Jersey

Pearson Prentice Hall™ is a trademark of Pearson Education, Inc.
Pearson® is a registered trademark of Pearson plc.
Prentice Hall® is a registered trademark of Pearson Education, Inc.

ISBN 0-13-203429-8
1 2 3 4 5 6 7 8 9 10   10 09 08 07 06

CONTENTS

HOW TO USE THIS BOOK

There are many vocabulary terms in *California Focus on Life Science*. Most of these terms are new to your students. This book is designed to help your students learn these words and their definitions.

This book is divided into chapters. For each chapter, the words that are highlighted in the Student Edition appear on one side of the page. The definitions of the words are on the back of the page. You can photocopy these pages and hand them out to your students. First, tear the pages out of the book. Then, using the "2→2-sided" setting on your printer, photocopy these pages. The students can then cut the words out to make vocabulary flashcards.

Your students can use the vocabulary flashcards as a tool to reinforce the key words and definitions as they learn them. Encourage your students to review their flashcards for a few minutes every day. The flashcards are also useful for reviewing an entire chapter or unit. Your students can use these flashcards in class by quizzing one another on the words and definitions.

On page 147, you will find a template. You can make copies of this template for your students. They can use the template to make their own vocabulary flashcards.

science

observing

quantitative observation

qualitative observation

inferring

predicting

classifying

making models

The process of using one or more of your senses to gather information. (p. 7)

A way of learning about the natural world and the knowledge gained through the process. (p. 6)

An observation that deals with characteristics that cannot be expressed in numbers. (p. 7)

An observation that deals with a number or amount. (p. 7)

The process of forecasting what will happen based on past experience or evidence. (p. 9)

The process of making an inference, an interpretation based on observations and prior knowledge. (p. 8)

The process of creating representations of complex objects or processes. (p. 11)

The process of grouping together items that are alike in some way. (p. 10)

scale model

life science

biology

development

structure

function

complementary

scientific inquiry

The study of living things. (p. 13)

A model that accurately shows the proportions between its parts. (p. 12)

The process of change that occurs during an organism's life to produce a more complex organism. (p. 15)

The study of life. (p. 13)

A process that enables an organism to survive. (p. 16)

The way an organism is put together as a whole. (p. 16)

The diverse ways in which scientists study the natural world and propose explanations based on evidence they gather. (p. 18)

Any two colors that combine to form white light or black pigment. (p. 16)

hypothesis

variable

controlled experiment

manipulated variable

responding variable

control

operational definition

data

A factor in an experiment that can change. (p. 20)

A possible explanation for a set of observations or answer to a scientific question; must be testable. (p. 19)

The one factor that a scientist changes during an experiment; also called independent variable. (p. 20)

An experiment in which only one variable is manipulated at a time. (p. 20)

The part of an experiment to which you can compare the results of the other tests. (p. 20)

The factor that changes as a result of changes to the manipulated, or independent, variable in an experiment; also called dependent variable. (p. 20)

Facts, figures, and other evidence gathered through observations. (p. 21)

A statement that describes how to measure a particular variable or how to define a particular term. (p. 20)

communicating

The process of sharing ideas
with others through writing
and speaking. (p. 21)

wave

energy

medium

vibration

crest

trough

amplitude

wavelength

The ability to do work or cause change. (p. 39)

A disturbance that transfers energy from place to place. (p. 39)

A repeated back-and-forth or up-and-down motion. (p. 39)

The material through which a wave travels. (p. 39)

The lowest part of a wave. (p. 40)

The highest part of a wave. (p. 40)

The distance between two corresponding parts of a wave. (p. 41)

The maximum distance the particles of a medium move away from their rest positions as a wave passes through the medium (p. 40)

frequency

hertz

electromagnetic wave

electromagnetic radiation

electromagnetic spectrum

visible light

transparent

translucent

Unit of measurement for frequency. (p. 41)

The number of complete waves that pass a given point in a certain amount of time. (p. 41)

The energy transferred through space by electromagnetic waves. (p. 42)

Waves that transfer electric and magnetic energy. (p. 42)

Electromagnetic waves that are visible to the human eye. (p. 43)

The complete range of electromagnetic waves placed in order of increasing frequency. (p. 43)

That which scatters light as it passes through. (p. 47)

That which transmits light without scattering it. (p. 47)

opaque

primary colors

secondary color

complementary colors

pigment

reflection

law of reflection

plane mirror

Three colors that can be used to make any other color. (p. 49)

That which reflects or absorbs all of the light that strikes it. (p. 47)

Any two colors that combine to form white light or black pigment. (p. 49)

Any color produced by combining equal amounts of any two primary colors. (p. 49)

The bouncing back of an object or wave when it hits a surface through which it cannot pass. (p. 53)

A colored chemical compound that absorbs light and can be used to color other materials. (p. 49)

A flat mirror that produces an upright, virtual image the same size as an object. (p. 54)

The rule that the angle of reflection equals the angle of incidence. (p. 53)

image

virtual image

concave mirror

optical axis

focal point

real image

convex mirror

refraction

An upright image formed where rays of light appear to meet or come from. (p. 54)

A copy of an object formed by reflected or refracted rays of light. (p. 54)

An imaginary line that divides a mirror in half. (p. 55)

A mirror with a surface that curves inward. (p. 55)

An upside-down image formed where rays of light meet. (p. 55)

The point at which light rays parallel to the optical axis meet, or appear to meet, after being reflected (or refracted) by a mirror (or a lens). (p. 55)

The bending of waves as they enter a new medium at an angle. (p. 57)

A mirror with a surface that curves outward. (p. 56)

lens

convex lens

concave lens

cornea

pupil

iris

retina

rods

A lens that is thicker in the center than at the edges. (p. 59)

A curved piece of glass or other transparent material that is used to refract light. (p. 58)

The clear tissue that covers the front of the eye. (p. 63)

A lens that is thinner in the center than at the edges. (p. 60)

The circular structure that surrounds the pupil and regulates the amount of light entering the eye. (p. 63)

The opening through which light enters the eye. (p. 63)

Light-sensitive cells in the retina that work best in dim light and enable you to see black, white, and gray. (p. 63)

A sheet of light-sensitive cells at the back of the eye on which an image is focused. (p. 63)

cones	nearsighted

farsighted	camera

telescope	refracting telescope

objective	eyepiece

A word used to describe a person who can see nearby things clearly, but objects at a distance are blurred. (p. 64)

Light-sensitive cells in the retina that work best in bright light and enable you to see color. (p. 63)

An optical instrument that uses lenses to focus light, and film to record an image of an object. (p. 66)

A word used to describe a person who can see distant objects clearly, but nearby objects appear blurry. (p. 64)

A telescope that uses two convex lenses to form images. (p. 67)

An optical instrument that forms enlarged images of distant objects (p. 67)

A lens that magnifies the image formed by the objective. (p. 67)

A lens that gathers light from an object and forms a real image. (p. 67)

reflecting telescope

microscope

electron microscope

An instrument that makes
small objects look larger.
(p. 68)

A telescope that uses a concave
mirror to gather light from
distant objects. (p. 67)

A microscope that uses a beam
of electrons to produce a
magnified image. (p. 69)

cell

cell theory

unicellular

multicellular

tissue

organ

organ system

organelle

A widely accepted explanation of the relationship between cells and living things. (p. 84)

The basic unit of structure and function in living things. (p. 81)

Consisting of many cells. (p. 85)

Made of a single cell. (p. 85)

A structure in the body that is composed of different kinds of tissue. (p. 85)

A group of similar cells that perform the same function. (p. 85)

A tiny cell structure that carries out a specific function within the cell. (p. 88)

A group of organs that work together to perform a major function in the body. (p. 85)

cell wall

cytoskeleton

cell membrane

nucleus

cytoplasm

mitochondria

endoplasmic reticulum

ribosome

A protein "framework" inside a cell that gives the cell a shape. (p. 89)

A rigid layer of nonliving material that surrounds the cells of plants and some other organisms. (p. 89)

The control center of the eukaryotic cell that directs the cell's activities and contains the information that determines the cell's form and function. (p. 92)

The outside cell boundary that controls which substances can enter or leave the cell. (p. 89)

Rod-shaped cell structures that convert energy in food molecules to energy the cell can use to carry out its functions. (p. 93)

The material within a cell apart from the nucleus. (p. 93)

A small grain-like structure in the cytoplasm of a cell where proteins are made. (p. 93)

A cell structure that forms passageways in which proteins and other materials are carried through the cell. (p. 93)

Golgi body

chloroplast

vacuole

lysosome

element

compound

carbohydrate

lipid

The phylum whose members have a notochord, a nerve cord, and slits in their throat area at some point in their lives. (p. 94)

A structure in a cell that receives proteins and other newly formed materials from the endoplasmic reticulum, packages them, and distributes them to other parts of the cell. (p.94)

A small, round cell structure containing chemicals that break down large food particles into smaller ones. (p. 94)

A sac inside a cell that acts as a storage area. (p. 94)

Two or more elements that are chemically combined. (p. 98)

Any substance that cannot be broken down into simpler substances. (p. 97)

Energy-rich organic compound, such as fat, oil, or wax, that is made of carbon, hydrogen, and oxygen. (p. 99)

An energy-rich organic compound made of the elements carbon, hydrogen, and oxygen. (p. 99)

protein

amino acid

enzyme

nucleic acid

DNA

RNA

selectively permeable

diffusion

A small molecule that is linked chemically to other amino acids to form proteins. (p. 100)

Large, organic molecule made of carbon, hydrogen, oxygen, nitrogen, and sometimes sulfur. (p. 100)

Very large organic molecule made of carbon, oxygen, hydrogen, nitrogen, and phosphorus, that contains the instructions cells need to carry out all the functions of life. (p. 101)

A protein that speeds up chemical reactions in a living thing. (p. 100)

Ribonucleic acid; a nucleic acid that plays an important role in the production of proteins. (p. 101)

Deoxyribonucleic acid; the genetic material that carries information about an organism and is passed from parent to offspring. (p. 101)

The process by which molecules move from an area of higher concentration to an area of lower concentration. (p. 103)

A property of cell membranes that allows some substances to pass through, while others cannot. (p. 102)

osmosis

passive transport

active transport

The movement of materials through a cell membrane without using the cell's energy. (p. 106)

The diffusion of water molecules through a selectively permeable membrane. (p. 104)

The movement of materials through a cell membrane using energy. (p. 106)

photosynthesis

autotroph

heterotroph

pigment

chlorophyll

stomata

respiration

fermentation

An organism that makes its own food. (p. 119)

The process by which a cell captures energy in sunlight and uses it to make food. (p. 119)

A colored chemical compound that absorbs light and can be used to color other materials. (p. 120)

An organism that cannot make its own food. (p. 119)

Small openings on a leaf through which oxygen and carbon dioxide can move. (p. 121)

The main photosynthetic pigment found in the chloroplasts of plants, algae, and some bacteria. (p. 120)

The process by which cells break down molecules to release energy without using oxygen. (p. 126)

The process by which cells break down simple food molecules such as glucose to release the energy they contain. (p. 124)

cell cycle

interphase

replication

mitosis

chromosome

cytokinesis

differentiation

stem cell

The stage of the cell cycle that takes place before cell division occurs. (p. 130)

The regular sequence of growth and division that cells undergo. (p. 130)

The stage of the cell cycle during which the cell's nucleus divides into two new nuclei and one copy of the DNA is distributed into each daughter cell. (p. 131)

The process by which a cell makes a copy of the DNA in its nucleus. (p. 130)

The final stage of the cell cycle, in which the cell's cytoplasm divides, distributing the organelles into each of the two new cells. (p. 134)

A double rod of condensed chromatin. (p. 131)

A cell that can differentiate throughout life. (p. 140)

The process by which cells change in structure and become capable of carrying out specialized functions. (p. 138)

heredity

trait

genetics

fertilization

purebred

gene

alleles

dominant allele

A characteristic that an organism can pass on to its offspring through its genes. (p. 154)

The passing of traits from parents to offspring. (p. 154)

The joining of a sperm and egg. (p. 155)

The scientific study of heredity. (p. 154)

The set of information that controls a trait; a segment of DNA on a chromosome that codes for a specific trait. (p. 157)

The offspring of many generations that have the same traits. (p. 155)

An allele whose trait always shows up in the organism when the allele is present. (p. 157)

The different forms of a gene. (p. 157)

recessive allele

hybrid

probability

Punnet square

phenotype

genotype

homozygous

heterozygous

An organism that has two different alleles for a trait; an organism that is heterozygous for a particular trait. (p. 158)

An allele that is masked when a dominant allele is present. (p. 157)

A chart that shows all the possible combinations of alleles that can result from a genetic cross. (p. 164)

A number that describes how likely it is that an event will occur. (p. 162)

An organism's genetic makeup, or allele combinations. (p. 166)

An organism's physical appearance, or visible traits. (p. 166)

Having two different alleles for a trait. (p. 166)

Having two identical alleles for a trait. (p. 166)

codominance

sexual reproduction

diploid

meiosis

messenger RNA

transfer RNA

mutation

A reproductive process that involves two parents that combine their genetic material to produce a new organism, which differs from both parents. (p. 170)

A condition in which neither of two alleles of a gene is dominant or recessive. (p. 167)

The process that occurs in the formation of sex cells (sperm and egg) by which the number of chromosomes is reduced by half. (p. 172)

Describes a cell that has two sets of chromosomes, one from each parent. (p. 171)

RNA in the cytoplasm that carries an amino acid to the ribosome and adds it to the growing protein chain. (p. 177)

RNA that copies the coded message from DNA in the nucleus and carries the message into the cytoplasm. (p. 177)

A change in a gene or chromosome. (p. 180)

multiple alleles

sex chromosomes

sex-linked gene

carrier

genetic disorder

pedigree

karyotype

selective breeding

A pair of chromosomes carrying genes that determine whether a person is male or female. (p. 195)

Three or more forms of a gene that code for a single trait. (p. 194)

A person who has one recessive allele. (p. 197)

A gene that is carried on the X or Y chromosome. (p. 196)

A chart or "family tree" that tracks which members of a family have a particular trait. (p. 201)

An abnormal condition that a person inherits through genes or chromosomes. (p. 199)

The process of selecting a few organisms with desired traits to serve as parents of the next generation. (p. 206)

A picture of all the chromosomes in a cell arranged in pairs. (p. 202)

inbreeding

hybridization

clone

genetic engineering

gene therapy

genome

A selective breeding method in which two genetically different individuals are crossed.
(p. 206)

A selective breeding method in which two individuals with identical or similar sets of alleles are crossed. (p. 206)

The transfer of a gene from the DNA of one organism into another organism, in order to produce an organism with desired traits. (p. 208)

An organism that is genetically identical to the organism from which it was produced.
(p. 207)

All of the DNA in one cell of an organism. (p. 210)

The insertion of working copies of a gene into the cells of a person with a genetic disorder in an attempt to correct the disorder. (p. 209)

species	**fossil**
adaptation	**evolution**
scientific theory	**natural selection**
variation	**comparative anatomy**

The preserved remains or traces of an organism that lived in the past. (p. 225)

A group of organisms that are physically similar and can mate with each other and produce offspring that can also mate and produce. (p. 225)

The gradual change in a species over time. (p. 228)

A behavior or physical characteristic that allows an organism to survive or reproduce in its environment. (p. 227)

A process by which individuals that are better adapted to their environment are more likely to survive and reproduce than others of the same species. (p. 229)

A well-tested concept that explains a wide range of observations. (p. 228)

The comparison of the structures of different organisms. (p. 235)

Any difference between individuals of the same species. (p. 229)

homogolous structures

petrified fossil

mold

cast

paleontologist

gradualism

punctuated equilibria

habitat

A fossil formed when minerals replace all or part of an organism. (p. 236)

Body parts that are structured similar in related species and that provide evidence for a common ancestor. (p. 235)

A type of fossil that forms when a mold becomes filled in with minerals that then harden. (p. 236)

A type of fossil formed when a shell or other hard part of an organism dissolves, leaving an empty space in the shape of the part. (p. 236)

The theory that evolution occurs slowly but steadily. (p. 240)

A scientist who studies fossils. (p. 238)

The specific environment that provides the things an organism needs to live, grow, and reproduce. (p. 242)

The theory that species evolve during short periods of rapid change. (p. 240)

extinct

classification

taxonomy

binomial nomenclature

genus

prokaryote

eukaryote

branching tree diagram

The process of grouping things based on their similarities. (p. 249)

A word used to describe a species if no members of that species are still alive. (p. 245)

The system for naming organisms in which each organism is given a unique, two-part scientific name. (p. 250)

The scientific study of how living things are classified. (p. 249)

An organism whose cells lack a nucleus and some other cell structures. (p. 253)

A classification grouping that consists of a number of similar, closely related species. (p. 250)

A diagram that shows how scientists think different groups of organisms are related. (p. 255)

An organism whose cells contain nuclei. (p. 253)

**shared derived
characteristic**

A characteristic—usually a homologous structure—shared by all organisms in a group. (p.256)

geology

erosion

uniformitarianism

igneous rock

sedimentary rock

metamorphic rock

rock cycle

magma

The process by which water, ice, or wind break down rocks and carry the pieces away. (p. 268)

The study of the structure of planet Earth and the forces that make and shape Earth. (p. 268)

A type of rock that forms from the cooling of molten rock at or below the surface. (p. 269)

The geologic principle that the same geologic processes that operate today operated in the past to change Earth's surface. (p. 269)

A type of rock that forms from an existing rock that is changed by heat, pressure, or chemical reactions. (p. 269)

Rock formed of hardened layers of sediments. (p. 269)

Molten material beneath Earth's surface. (p. 270)

A series of processes on the surface and inside Earth that slowly change rocks from one kind to another. (p. 270)

lava

relative age

absolute age

law of superposition

extrusion

intrusion

fault

unconformity

The age of rock compared to the ages of rock layers. (p. 272)

Liquid magma that reaches the surface. (p. 270)

The geologic principle that states that in horizontal layers of sedimentary rock, each layer is older than the layer above it and younger than the layer below it. (p. 273)

The age of a rock given as the number of years since the rock formed. (p. 272)

An igneous rock layer formed when magma hardens beneath Earth's surface. (p. 274)

An igneous rock layer formed when lava flows onto Earth's surface and hardens. (p. 274)

A place where an old, eroded rock surface is in contact with a newer rock layer. (p. 275)

A break or crack in Earth's crust along which the rocks move. (p. 274)

inclusion

index fossil

atom

element

radioactive decay

half-life

plate

theory of plate tectonics

Fossils of widely distributed organisms that lived during only one short period. (p. 276)

A piece of rock that is contained in another rock; an inclusion is younger than the rock containing it. (p. 275)

Any substance that cannot be broken down into simpler substances. (p. 280)

The smallest particle of an element. (p. 280)

The time it takes for half of the atoms in a radioactive element to decay. (p. 280)

The breakdown of a radioactive element, releasing particles and energy. (p. 280)

Theory that states Earth's plates move slowly in different directions. (p. 284)

One of the major pieces of Earth's rocky outer layer on which continents and oceans move. (p. 284)

continental drift

geologic time scale

era

period

invertebrate

vertebrate

amphibian

reptile

A record of the geologic events and life forms in Earth's history. (p. 286)

The very slow motion of the continents. (p. 284)

One of the units of geologic time into which geologists divide eras. (p. 286)

One of the three long units of geologic time between the Precambrian and the present. (p. 286)

An animal that has a backbone. (p. 289)

An animal that does not have a backbone. (p. 289)

An animal that lays eggs and has lungs and scaly skin. (p. 290)

An animal that spends its early life in water and its adult life on land. (p. 290)

mass extinction

mammal

An endothermic vertebrate with a four-chambered heart, skin covered with fur or hair, and young fed with milk from the mother's body. (p. 294)

When many types of living things become extinct at the same time. (p. 291)

virus

host

parasite

bacteriophage

vaccine

bacteria

flagellum

binary fission

The organism that a parasite or virus lives in or on. (p. 318)

A tiny, nonliving particle that invades and then reproduces inside a living cell. (p. 318)

A virus that infects bacteria. (p. 319)

The organism that benefits by living on or in a host in a parasitism interaction. (p. 318)

Single-celled organisms that lack a nucleus; prokaryotes. (p. 326)

A substance used in a vaccination that consists of weakened or killed pathogens that can trigger the immune system into action. (p. 323)

A form of asexual reproduction in which one cell divides to form two identical cells. (p. 328)

A long, whiplike structure that helps a cell to move. (p. 326)

asexual reproduction

sexual reproduction

conjugation

endospore

pasteurization

decomposer

protist

protozoan

A reproductive process that involves two parents that combine their genetic material to produce a new organism, which differs from both parents. (p. 328)

A reproductive process that involves only one parent and produces offspring that are identical to the parent. (p. 328)

A small, rounded, thick-walled, resting cell that forms inside a bacterial cell. (p. 329)

The process in which a unicellular organism transfers some of its genetic material to another unicellular organism. (p. 328)

An organism that breaks down chemicals from wastes and dead organisms. (p. 332)

A process of heating food to a temperature that is high enough to kill most harmful bacteria without changing the taste of the food. (p. 331)

An animal-like protist. (p. 335)

A eukaryotic organism that cannot be classified as an animal, plant, or fungus. (p. 335)

pseudopod

contractile vacuole

cilia

symbiosis

mutualism

algae

spore

fungi

The cell structure that collects extra water from the cytoplasm and then expels it from the cell. (p. 336)

A "false foot" or temporary bulge of cytoplasm used for feeding and movement in some protozoans. (p. 336)

A close relationship between two organisms of different species that benefits at least one of the organisms. (p. 338)

The hairlike projections on the outside of cells that move in a wavelike manner. (p. 337)

Plantlike protists. (p. 339)

A close relationship between organisms of two species in which both organisms benefit. (p. 338)

A eukaryotic organism that has cell walls, uses spores to reproduce, and is a heterotroph that feeds by absorbing its food. (p. 344)

A tiny cell that is able to grow into a new organism. (p. 342)

hyphae

fruiting body

budding

lichen

The reproductive structure of a fungus that contains many hyphae and produces spores. (p. 346)

The branching, threadlike tubes that make up the bodies of multicellular fungi. Consisting of many cells. (p. 345)

The combination of a fungus and either an alga or an autotrophic bacterium that live together in a mutualistic relationship. (p. 349)

A form of asexual reproduction of yeast in which a new cell grows out of the body of a parent. (p. 346)

cuticle	vascular tissue
zygote	vegetative reproduction
nonvascular plant	sporophyte
gametophyte	rhizoid

The internal transporting tissue in some plants that is made up of tubelike structures. (p. 365)

The waxy, waterproof layer that covers the leaves and stems of most plants. (p. 364)

Reproduction in plants by asexual methods. (p. 365)

A fertilized egg, produced by the joining of a sperm and an egg. (p. 365)

The stage in the life cycle of a plant in which the plant produces spores. (p. 368)

A low-growing plant that lacks true vascular tissue. (p. 366)

A thin, rootlike structure that anchors a moss and absorbs water and nutrients. (p. 371)

The stage in the life cycle of a plant in which the plant produces gametes, or sex cells. (p. 368)

frond

phloem

xylem

pollen

seed

embryo

cotyledon

germination

The vascular tissue through which food moves in some plants. (p. 376)

The leaf of a fern plant. (p. 373)

Tiny particles (male gametophytes) produced by seed plants that contain the cells that later become sperm cells. (p. 376)

The vascular tissue through which water and nutrients move in some plants. (p. 376)

A young organism that develops from a zygote. (p. 377)

The plant structure that contains a young plant inside a protective covering. (p. 376)

The sprouting of the embryo from a seed that occurs where the embryo resumes growth. (p. 379)

A second leaf. (p. 377)

root cap

cambium

transpiration

gymnosperm

cone

ovule

pollination

angiosperm

A layer of cells in a plant that produces new phloem and xylem cells. (p. 383)

A structure that covers the tip of a root protecting the root from injury. (p. 381)

A plant that produces seeds that are not enclosed by a protective fruit. (p. 388)

The process by which water is lost through a plant's leaves. (p. 385)

A structure that contains an egg cell. (p. 390)

The reproductive structure of a gymnosperm. (p. 390)

A flowering plant that produces seeds enclosed in a protective structure. (p. 392)

The transfer of pollen from male reproductive structures to female reproductive structures in plants. (p. 390)

flower

sepal

petal

stamen

pistil

ovary

fruit

monocot

A leaflike structure that encloses the bud of a flower. (p. 392)

The reproductive structure of an angiosperm. (p. 392)

A male reproductive part of a flower. (p. 392)

A colorful, leaflike structure of some flowers. (p. 392)

A flower structure that encloses and protects ovules and seeds as they develop. (p. 393)

The female reproductive part of a flower. (p. 393)

An angiosperm with one seed leaf. (p. 396)

The ripened ovary and other structures of an angiosperm that enclose one or more seeds. (p. 394)

dicot

An angiosperm that has two
seed leaves. (p. 396)

anatomy

physiology

bilateral symmetry

radial symmetry

vertebrate

invertebrate

phylum

larva

The study of the functions in organisms. (p. 411)

The study of the structure of organisms. (p. 411)

The quality of having many lines of symmetry that all pass through a central point. (p. 414)

Body plan with two halves that are mirror images. (p. 414)

An animal that does not have a backbone. (p. 416)

An animal that has a backbone. (p. 416)

The immature form of an animal that looks very different from the adult. (p. 418)

One of the major groups into which biologists classify members of a kingdom. (p. 416)

cnidarian

polyp

medusa

brain

parasite

host

anus

closed circulatory system

The cnidarian body plan is characterized by a vaselike shape and is usually adapted for life attached to an underwater surface. (p. 419)

An invertebrate animal that uses stinging cells to capture food and defend itself. (p. 419)

The part of the central nervous system that is located in the skull and controls most functions in the body. (p. 425)

The cnidarian body plan having a bowl shape and adapted for a free-swimming life. (p. 419)

The organism a parasite or virus lives in or on. (p. 426)

The organism that benefits by living on or in a host in a parasitism interaction. (p. 426)

A circulatory system in which blood moves only within a connected network of tubes called blood vessels. (p. 429)

A muscular opening at the end of the rectum through which waste material is eliminated from the body. (p. 428)

mollusk

open circulatory system

gill

gastropod

radula

bivalve

cephalopod

arthropod

A circulatory system in which the heart pumps blood into a short vessel that opens into spaces in the body, and with which blood is not confined to blood vessels. (p. 430)

An invertebrate with a soft, unsegmented body; most are protected by a hard outer shell. (p. 430)

A mollusk with a single shell or no shell. (p. 431)

An organ that removes oxygen from water. (p. 430)

A mollusk that has two shells held together by hinges and strong muscles. (p. 431)

A flexible ribbon of tiny teeth in mollusks. (p. 431)

An invertebrate that has an external skeleton, a segmented body, and jointed appendages. (p. 434)

An ocean-dwelling mollusk whose foot is adapted as tentacles. (p. 432)

exoskeleton

molting

antenna

crustacean

metamorphosis

arachnid

abdomen

insect

The process of shedding an outgrown exoskeleton. (p. 435)

A waxy, waterproof outer shell or outer skeleton that protects the animal and helps prevent evaporation of water. (p. 435)

An anthropod that has two or three body sections, five or more pairs of legs, and two pairs of antennae. (p. 437)

An appendage on the head of an arthropod that contains sense organs. (p. 436)

An anthropod with two body sections, four pairs of legs, and no antennae. (p. 438)

A process in which an animal's body undergoes dramatic changes in form during its life cycle. (p. 437)

An arthropod with three body sections, six legs, one pair of antennae, and usually one or two pairs of wings. (p. 439)

The hind section of an arthropod's body that contains its reproductive organs and part of its digestive tract. (p. 438)

thorax

complete metamorphosis

pupa

gradual metamorphosis

nymph

echinoderm

endoskeleton

water vascular system

A type of metamorphosis characterized by four dramatically different states. (p. 440)

An arthropod's midsection, to which its wings and legs are attached. (p. 439)

A type of metamorphosis in which an egg hatches into a nymph that resembles an adult, and which has no distinctly different larval stage. (p. 440)

The third stage of complete metamorphosis, in which an insect changes from a larva to an adult. (p. 440)

A radially symmetrical invertebrate that has an internal skeleton and a water vascular system. (p. 443)

A stage of gradual metamorphosis that usually resembles the adult insect. (p. 440)

A system of fluid-filled tubes in an echinoderm's body. (p. 444)

An internal skeleton. (p. 443)

tube feet

Extensions of an echinoderm's water vascular system that stick out from the body and function in movement and obtaining food. (p. 444)

chordate

notochord

vertebrae

ectotherm

endotherm

fish

cartilage

swim bladder

A flexible rod that supports a chordate's back. (p. 456)

The phylum whose members have a notochord, a nerve cord, and slits in their throat area at some point in their lives. (p. 456)

An animal whose body does not produce much internal heat. (p. 459)

The small bones that make up the backbone. (p. 457)

An ectothermic vertebrate that lives in the water and has fins. (p. 463)

An animal whose body controls and regulates its temperature by controlling the internal heat it produces. (p. 460)

An internal, gas-filled organ that helps a bony fish stabilize its body at different water depths. (p. 466)

A connective tissue that is more flexible than bone and that protects the ends of bones and keeps them from rubbing together. (p. 465)

amphibian

tadpole

lung

atrium

ventricle

habitat

reptile

kidney

The larval form of a frog or a toad. (p. 469)

An animal that spends its early life in water and its adult life on land. (p. 468)

Each of the two upper chambers of the heart that receives blood that comes into the heart. (p. 470)

An organ found in air-breathing vertebrates that exchanges oxygen and carbon dioxide with the blood. (p. 470)

The specific environment that provides things an organism needs to live, grow, and reproduce. (p. 471)

A lower chamber of the heart that pumps blood out of the lungs and body. (p. 470)

A major organ of the excretory system that removes urea and other wastes from the blood. (p. 473)

An animal that lays eggs and has lungs and scaly skin. (p. 473)

urine

amniotic egg

bird

contour feather

down feather

crop

gizzard

mammal

An egg with a shell and internal membranes that keep the embryo moist. (p. 474)

A watery fluid produced by the kidneys that contains urea and other wastes. (p. 473)

A large feather that helps give shape to a bird's body. (p. 481)

An endothermic vertebrate that has feathers and a four-chambered heart, and lays eggs. (p. 481)

A bird's internal storage pouch that allows it to store food inside its body after swallowing it. (p. 483)

A short, fluffy feather that traps heat and keeps a bird warm. (p. 481)

An endothermic vertebrate with a four-chambered heart, skin covered with fur or hair, and young fed with milk from the mother's body. (p. 486)

A muscular, thick-walled part of a bird's stomach that squeezes and grinds partially digested food. (p. 483)

mammary gland

diaphragm

monotreme

marsupial

gestation period

placental mammal

placenta

A large muscle located at the bottom of a mammal's rib cage that functions in breathing. (p. 488)

An organ in female mammals that produces milk for the mammal's young. (p. 487)

A mammal whose young are born alive at an early stage of development, and which usually continue to develop in a pouch on their mother's body. (p. 490)

A mammal that lays eggs. (p. 490)

A mammal that develops inside its mother's body until its body systems can function independently. (p. 491)

The length of time between fertilization and birth of a mammal. (p. 490)

A membrane that becomes the link between the developing embryo or fetus and the mother. (p. 491)

muscle tissue

nervous tissue

connective tissue

epithelial tissue

organ system

digestion

kidney

nephron

A body tissue that carries electrical messages back and forth between the brain and every other part of the body. (p. 510)

A body tissue that contracts or shortens, making body parts move. (p. 510)

A body tissue that covers the surfaces of the body, inside and out. (p. 510)

A body tissue that provides support for the body and connects all of its parts. (p. 510)

The processes by which the body breaks down food into small nutrient molecules. (p. 512)

A group of organs that work together to perform a major function in the body. (p. 510)

Small filtering structure found in the kidneys that removes wastes from blood and produces urine. (p. 513)

A major organ of the excretory system that removes urea and other wastes from the blood. (p. 513)

| urinary bladder | pathogen |

| antibody | immunity |

| homeostasis | stress |

| skeleton | vertebrae |

An organism that causes disease. (p. 514)

A sacklike muscular organ that stores urine until it is eliminated from the body. (p. 513)

The body's ability to destroy pathogens. (p. 514)

A protein produced by a B cell of the immune system that destroys pathogens. (p. 514)

The reaction of a person's body to potentially threatening, challenging, or disturbing events. (p. 517)

The maintenance of stable internal conditions in an organism. (p. 516)

The small bones that makeup the backbone. (p. 519)

The inner framework made of all the bones of the body. (p. 518)

joint

ligament

cartilage

compact bone

spongy bone

marrow

osteoporosis

involuntary muscle

Strong connective tissue that holds bones together in moveable joints. (p. 521)

The place in the body where two bones come together. (p. 520)

Hard, dense bone tissue that is beneath the outer membrane of a bone. (p. 522)

A connective tissue that is more flexible than bone and that protects the ends of bones and keeps them from rubbing together. (p. 521)

The soft, connective tissue that fills the internal spaces in bone. (p. 522)

Layer of bone tissue having many small spaces and found just inside the layer of compact bone. (p. 522)

A muscle that is not under conscious control. (p. 526)

A condition in which the body's bones become weak and break easily. (p. 525)

voluntary muscle

skeletal muscle

tendon

striated muscle

smooth muscle

cardiac muscle

force

work

A muscle that is attached to the bones of the skeleton and provides the force that moves the bones. (p. 528)

A muscle that is under conscious control. (p. 527)

A muscle that appears banded; also called skeletal muscle. (p. 528)

Strong connective tissue that attaches muscle to bone. (p. 528)

Muscle tissue found only in the heart. (p. 528)

Involuntary muscle found inside many internal organs of the body. (p. 528)

Force exerted on an object that causes it to move. (p. 533)

A push or pull exerted on an object. (p. 533)

machine

lever

fulcrum

effort force

effort distance

resistance force

resistance distance

mechanical advantage

A simple machine that consists of a rigid bar that pivots about a fixed point. (p. 534)

A device that changes the amount of force exerted or the distance over which a force is exerted. (p. 533)

The force you exert on a lever. (p. 534)

The fixed point around which a lever pivots. (p. 534)

The force a lever exerts on an object. (p. 534)

The distance you push down on a lever. (p. 534)

For a lever, the ratio of the resistance force to the effort force. (p. 536)

The distance a lever pushes up on an object. (p. 534)

effort arm

resistance arm

For a lever, the distance from the fulcrum to the resistance force. (p. 536)

For a lever, the distance from the fulcrum to the effort force. (p. 536)

cardiovascular system

heart

atrium

pacemaker

ventricle

valve

artery

capillary

A hollow, muscular organ that pumps blood throughout the body. (p. 554)

The body system that consists of the heart, blood vessels, and blood; circulatory system. (p. 552)

A group of cells located in the right atrium that sends out signals that make the heart muscle contract and that regulates heartbeat rate. (p. 555)

Each of the two upper chambers of the heart that receives blood that comes into the heart. (p. 555)

A flap of tissue in the heart or a vein that prevents blood from flowing backward. (p. 555)

A lower chamber of the heart that pumps blood out to the lungs and body. (p. 555)

A tiny blood vessel where substances are exchanged between the blood and the body cells. (p. 556)

A blood vessel that carries blood away from the heart. (p. 556)

vein

aorta

coronary artery

pulse

diffusion

pressure

blood pressure

plasma

The largest artery in the body.
(p. 557)

A blood vessel that carries blood back to the heart.
(p. 556)

The alternating expansion and relaxation of an artery wall as blood travels through an artery. (p. 558)

An artery that supplies blood to the heart itself. (p. 558)

The force exerted on a surface divided by the total area over which the force is exerted.
(p. 560)

The process by which molecules move from an area of higher concentration to an area of lower concentration.
(p. 559)

The liquid part of blood.
(p. 563)

The pressure that is exerted by the blood against the walls of blood vessels. (p. 560)

red blood cell

hemoglobin

white blood cell

platelet

shock

lymphatic system

lymph

lymph node

An iron-containing protein that binds chemically to oxygen molecules. (p. 564)

A cell in the blood that takes up oxygen in the lungs and delivers it to cells elsewhere in the body. (p. 564)

A cell fragment that plays an important part in forming blood clots. (p. 566)

A blood cell that fights disease. (p. 565)

A network of veinlike vessels that returns the fluid that leaks out of blood vessels to the bloodstream. (p. 568)

The failure of the circulatory system to provide adequate oxygen-rich blood to all parts of the body. (p. 566)

A small knob of tissue in the lymphatic system that filters lymph, trapping bacteria and other microorganisms that cause disease. (p. 569)

The fluid that the lymphatic system collects and returns to the bloodstream. (p. 568)

respiration

mucus

cilia

pharynx

trachea

bronchi

lungs

alveoli

A thick, sticky liquid produced by the body. (p. 573)

The process by which cells break down simple food molecules such as glucose to release the energy they contain. (p. 571)

The throat. (p. 573)

The hairlike projections on the outside of cells that move in a wavelike manner. (p. 573)

The passages that direct air into the lungs. (p. 574)

The windpipe; a passage through which air moves in the respiratory systems. (p. 574)

Tiny sacs of lung tissue specialized for the movement of gases between air and blood. (p. 574)

An organ found in air-breathing vertebrates that exchanges oxygen and carbon dioxide with blood. (p. 574)

diaphragm

larynx

vocal cords

atherosclerosis

heart attack

hypertension

stroke

emphysema

The voice box. (p. 578)

A large muscle located at the bottom of a mammal's rib cage that functions in breathing. (p. 576)

A condition in which the artery wall thickens from a buildup of fatty materials. (p. 581)

Folds of connective tissue that stretch across the opening of the larynx and produce a person's voice. (p. 578)

A disorder in which a person's blood pressure is consistently higher than normal; also called high blood pressure. (p. 582)

A condition in which blood flow to part of the heart muscle is blocked, causing heart cells to die. (p. 581)

A serious disease that destroys lung tissue and causes breathing difficulties. (p. 585)

Death of brain tissue that can result when a blood vessel in the brain is either blocked by a clot or bursts. (p. 583)

bronchitis

asthma

suffocation

pneumonia

A respiratory disorder in which the airways in the lungs narrow significantly. (p. 586)

An irritation of the breathing passages in which the small passages become narrower than normal and may be clogged with mucus. (p. 585)

An infection in which fluids accumulate in the alveoli, decreasing the lungs' ability to take in oxygen and remove carbon dioxide. (p. 587)

Dangerous condition in which insufficient gas exchange in the lungs leads to a lack of oxygen in the vital organs. (p. 586)

stimulus

response

neuron

nerve impulse

dendrite

axon

nerve

sensory neuron

An action or change in behavior that occurs in reaction to a stimulus. (p. 601)

A change or signal in an organism's surroundings that causes the organism to react. (p. 601)

The message carried by a neuron. (p. 602)

A cell that carries information through the nervous system. (p. 602)

A threadlike extension of a neuron that carries nerve impulses away from the cell body. (p. 602)

A threadlike extension of a neuron that carries nerve impulses toward the cell body. (p. 602)

A neuron that picks up stimuli from the internal or external environment and converts each stimulus into a nerve impulse. (p. 602)

A bundle of nerve fibers. (p. 602)

interneuron

motor neuron

synapse

central nervous system

peripheral nervous system

brain

spinal cord

cerebrum

A neuron that sends an impulse to a muscle or gland, causing the muscle or gland to react. (p. 602)

A neuron that carries nerve impulses from one neuron to another. (p. 602)

The division of the nervous system consisting of the brain and spinal cord. (p. 606)

The junction where one neuron can transfer an impulse to another structure. (p. 604)

The part of the central nervous system that is located in the skull and controls most functions in the body. (p. 607)

The division of the nervous system consisting of all of the nerves located outside the central nervous system. (p. 606)

The part of the brain that interprets input from the senses, controls movement, and carries out complex mental processes. (p. 608)

The thick column of nerve tissue that links the brain to most of the nerves in the peripheral nervous system. (p. 607)

cerebellum

brain stem

somatic nervous system

autonomic nervous system

reflex

concussion

cornea

pupil

The part of the brain that lies between the cerebellum and spinal cord, and controls the body's involuntary actions. (p. 608)

The part of the brain that coordinates muscle action and helps maintain balance. (p. 608)

The group of nerves in the peripheral nervous system that controls involuntary actions. (p. 611)

The group of nerves in the peripheral nervous system that controls voluntary actions. (p. 611)

A bruiselike injury of the brain that occurs when the soft tissue of the brain collides against the skull. (p. 613)

An automatic response that occurs rapidly and without conscious control. (p. 611)

The opening through which light enters the eye. (p. 615)

The clear tissue that covers the front of the eye. (p. 615)

iris

lens

retina

rods

cones

optic nerve

nearsightedness

farsightedness

A curved piece of glass or other transparent material that is used to refract light. (p. 615)

The circular structure that surrounds the pupil and regulates the amount of light entering the eye. (p. 615)

Receptor cells in the eye that work best in dim light and enable you to see black, white, and gray. (p. 616)

A sheet of sensitive cells at the back of the eye on which an image is focused. (p. 616)

The short, thick nerve in the eye through which rods and cones send electrical impulses to the brain. (p. 616)

Receptor cells in the eye that work best in bright light and enable you to see color. (p. 616)

The condition in which a person can see distant objects clearly. (p. 617)

The condition in which a person can see nearby objects clearly. (p. 617)

eardrum

hammer

anvil

stirrup

cochlea

semicircular canals

taste bud

drug

A small bone in the middle ear that transmits vibrations from the eardrum to the anvil; also called the malleus. (p. 619)

The membrane that separates the outer ear from the middle ear, and that vibrates when sound waves strike it. (p. 619)

A small bone in the middle ear that transmits vibrations from the anvil to a membrane of the inner ear; also called the "stapes." (p. 619)

A small bone in the middle ear that transmits vibrations from the hammer to the stirrup also called the "incus." (p. 619)

Structures in the inner ear that are responsible for the sense of balance. (p. 620)

A snail-shaped tube in the inner ear that is lined with receptor cells that respond to sound. (p. 619)

Any chemical taken into the body that causes changes in a person's body or behavior. (p. 624)

An organ on the tongue that contains receptors that detect chemicals in food. (p. 622)

drug abuse

tolerance

addiction

withdrawal

depressant

stimulant

alcoholism

A state in which a drug user needs larger amounts of the drug to produce the same effect on the body. (p. 625)

The deliberate misuse of drugs for purposes other than medical. (p. 624)

A period of adjustment that occurs when a drug-dependent person stops taking the drug. (p. 625)

A physical dependence on a substance. (p. 625)

A drug that speeds up body processes. (p. 626)

A drug that slows down the activity of the central nervous system. (p. 626)

A disease in which a person is both physically addicted to and emotionally dependent on alcohol. (p. 629)

endocrine gland

hormone

target cell

hypothalamus

pituitary gland

negative feedback

egg

sperm

A chemical product of an endocrine gland that produces a specific effect such as growth or development. (p. 641)

A structure of the endocrine system that produces and releases its chemical products directly into the bloodstream. (p. 641)

A part of the brain that links the nervous system and the endocrine system. (p. 642)

A cell in the body that recognizes a hormone's chemical structure. (p. 642)

A process in which a system is turned off by the condition it produces. (p. 644)

An endocrine gland that controls many body activities. (p. 644)

A male sex cell. (p. 649)

A female sex cell. (p. 649)

testis

testosterone

scrotum

semen

penis

urethra

ovary

estrogen

A hormone produced by the testes that controls the development of physical characteristics in mature men. (p. 650)

Organ of the male reproductive system in which sperm and testosterone are produced. (p. 650)

A mixture of sperm and fluids. (p. 651)

An external pouch of skin in which the testes are located. (p. 650)

A small tube through which urine flows from the body. (p. 651)

The organ through which both semen and urine leave the male body. (p. 651)

Organ of the female reproductive system in which eggs and estrogen are produced. (p. 652)

A hormone produced by the ovaries that controls the development of eggs and adult female characteristics. (p. 652)

fallopian tube

uterus

vagina

menstrual cycle

follicle

ovulation

menstruation

embryo

The hollow muscular organ of the female reproductive system in which a fertilized egg develops. (p. 653)

A passageway for eggs from an ovary to the uterus. (p. 652)

The cycle of changes that occurs in the female reproductive system, during which an egg develops and the uterus prepares for the arrival of a fertilized egg. (p. 653)

A muscular passageway leading to the outside of the body; also called the birth canal. (p. 653)

The process in which a mature egg is released from the ovary into a fallopian tube. (p. 654)

A grouping of cells in which an egg matures in an ovary. (p. 654)

A developing human during the first eight weeks after fertilization. (p. 657)

The process in which the thickened lining of the uterus breaks down, and blood and tissue then pass out of the female body. (p. 654)

differentiation

fetus

amniotic sac

placenta

umbilical cord

adolescence

puberty

A developing human from the ninth week of development until birth. (p. 658)

The process by which cells change in structure and become capable of carrying out specialized functions. (p. 657)

A membrane that becomes the link between the developing embryo or fetus and the mother. (p. 659)

A fluid-filled sac that cushions and protects a developing embryo and fetus in the uterus. (p. 659)

The stage of development between childhood and adulthood when children become adults physically and mentally. (p. 662)

A ropelike structure that forms between the embryo or fetus and the placenta. (p. 659)

The period of sexual development in which the body becomes able to reproduce. (p. 663)